Pete Morgan is visiting the Caribbean with his mother and father. The Morgans are having a holiday for six months on their boat, *Summer Sun*.

Pete's mother is a teacher. Every day she teaches him for three hours.

One morning Pete is washing the boat at Blue Sea Island.

'It's nine o'clock,' his mother says. 'Let's do some work.'

There is a computer on *Summer Sun*. Pete is looking at it.

'What's "*The Story of Your Family*"?' Pete asks.

'It's a history website,' his mother answers.

'History is *boring*,' Pete says. 'Can we do some Chinese, please? I *like* Chinese.'

Mrs Morgan smiles. 'OK,' she says.

Later, Pete goes to a beach near the boat. He takes his metal-detector and finds an old knife.

A pirate with long white hair is watching Pete. He is standing behind some trees.

He sees the knife and smiles.

Then suddenly he sees Mr Morgan.

'*Pete!*' Mr Morgan says.

Pete looks at his father.

'There's a small town near here,' Mr Morgan says. 'Your mother and I need to do some shopping. Can you stay with the boat this afternoon?'

'Yes,' Pete says. 'That's not a problem. I need to write some e-mails.'

'Good,' Mr Morgan smiles. 'See you later.'

At three o'clock Pete is writing an e-mail on *Summer Sun*.

'The Caribbean is fantastic,' it says. 'Every day we …'

Suddenly, the door opens. Pete's mouth opens too.

'Who are *you*?!' Pete asks.

'My name is Tom Carter,' the pirate from the beach says.

'Come with me.' He looks at Pete's metal-detector.

'And bring your machine too.'

Pete and Tom walk to the beach. There is a small boat behind some trees. Tom takes Pete to a very *big* boat.

'The *White Rose*,' Pete reads. 'Are you a ghost?!' he asks.

'Yes,' Tom says. 'The *White Rose*'s men only walk and talk for one day every hundred years. Usually we live under the water.'

Pete's eyes are big, but he doesn't answer.

On the *White Rose*, Pete meets its captain. The captain only has one leg.

'Our treasure is on a small island near here, but we can't find it,' he says. 'We only have one day. Can you and your machine help us?'

Pete looks at the captain's white face and hat.

'Yes,' he says very quietly. 'OK.'

One hour later, Pete and the pirates are on a small island. Pete looks for their treasure with his metal-detector. The pirates wait and watch.

Suddenly … *Beeeeep!* … Pete finds it.

'That's fantastic, boy!' the captain says. 'You're a pirate now.'

Tom looks up. 'A storm is coming,' he says.

The storm arrives. The pirates quickly go back to the *White Rose* with Pete.

On the boat they look at their treasure.

'This is a fantastic day!' Pete thinks. Then he looks at the dark sea.

Summer Sun is near the *White Rose* now.

'Oh no! That's my mother and father's boat,' he says.

The *White Rose*'s captain looks too. *Summer Sun* is going up and down in the big storm.

'*What can I do?*' Pete asks.

The captain talks quietly. 'It's OK, boy,' he says. 'Pirates help pirates.' Then he looks at Tom. 'Take the long rope, Mr Carter,' he says.

'Yes, Captain,' Tom answers.

Suddenly, Tom is in the water with a long, heavy rope.

It is raining and the sea is black.

'Swim, Tom! *SWIM!*' the pirates all say.

Pete closes his eyes. He can't watch.

Then the captain says, 'Look! He's on your boat.'

Pete opens his eyes again and smiles.

Tom has the rope in his hand. '*CATCH!*' he says.

After the storm, the pirates take Pete and *Summer Sun* back to Blue Sea Island.

'Thank you, Captain …' Pete stops and smiles. '… I don't know your name!'

'It's Pete Morgan,' the captain says.

'*But that*'s MY *name too!*'

Time stops. Suddenly Pete says, 'Come with me.'

Pete looks at the history website on his computer. After a short time, he smiles.

'This is fantastic!' he says. 'You're my great-great-great-great-great-great-*great*-grandfather!'

'*Am I?*' Captain Morgan says. He is smiling too.

Then Tom walks into the room and says, 'Evening's coming, Captain. We need to say goodbye.'

At six o'clock, Pete's new friends go under the water.

An hour later, his mother and father come back.

'Are you OK?' Mrs Morgan asks.

'Yes,' Pete answers. They talk about the storm.

Later he asks, 'Can we do some history tomorrow?'

'But you don't like history,' Mrs Morgan answers.

'I do now,' Pete says and smiles. '*It's fantastic!*'

ACTIVITIES

Pages 1–7

Before you read

1 Read the Word List at the back of the book. What are the twenty words in your language? Find them in a dictionary.

2 Look at the pictures, then talk to a friend. What do you think?

  a Where is Pete on page 1?

  b Who is watching him on page 3?

  c What is the *White Rose* on page 6?

  d Why do the pirates need Pete on page 7?

While you read

3 Here are eight sentences. Are they right (✔) or wrong (✗)?

  a The Morgans are on holiday for three months. .....

  b Their boat is *Blue Sea Island.* .....

  c Pete is a teacher. .....

  d Tom Carter is a ghost. .....

  e Pete has a metal-detector. .....

  f Pete goes shopping with his mother and father. .....

  g The captain of the *White Rose* only has one leg. .....

  h The pirates can't find their treasure. .....

After you read

4 Pete Morgan is your friend. He sends you an e-mail. What does he say about his Caribbean holiday? Does he like the hot sun / the food / the people? Write the e-mail.

Pages 8–14

Before you read

5 Look at the pictures, then talk to a friend. What do you think?

- **a** Why are the pirates happy on page 8?
- **b** What is Pete looking at on page 9?
- **c** Who is in the water on page 11?
- **d** Where is the *White Rose* going on page 14?

While you read

6 What comes first? And then? Write the numbers (1–10).

- **a** Pete looks at the computer on *Summer Sun.* .....
- **b** Pete says, 'Oh no!' .....
- **c** Captain Morgan says, 'Am I?' .....
- **d** Tom Carter says, 'We need to say goodbye.' .....
- **e** Pete finds the pirates' treasure. ..*1*..
- **f** The *White Rose* goes under the water again. .....
- **g** Tom Carter swims to *Summer Sun.* .....
- **h** Mrs Morgan asks Pete, 'Are you OK?' .....
- **i** A storm arrives. .....
- **j** The pirates take Pete and *Summer Sun* back to Blue Sea Island. .....

After you read

7 A metal-detector, a storm, a rope and a computer are all very important in this story. Why? Write your answers.

8 What is the story of *Pete and the Pirates*? Write one sentence for every picture in the book.

WORD LIST *with example sentences*

beach (n) They are on holiday near the sea. There is a beautiful *beach*.

boring (adj) This film isn't *boring*. It's very interesting.

captain (n) There is always a *captain* on an aeroplane or a boat.

computer (n) You can work and play games on a computer.

e-mail (n) I send four or five *e-mails* every day.

fantastic (adj) I love football. It's *fantastic*!

ghost (n) This house is very old. Does it have a *ghost*?

great-grandfather (n) Your father's father is your grandfather. His father is your *great-grandfather*.

help (v) Please *help* me! I can't open the door.

history (n) Winston Churchill is a famous person in British *history*.

hour (n) There are twenty-four *hours* in a day.

island (v) Cuba is a big *island* in the Caribbean Sea.

machine (n) Cars, telephones and televisions are all *machines*.

metal-detector (n) The children are in the garden. They are looking for old money with my *metal-detector*.

need (v + to + infinitive) This is a long walk. I *need* to sit down.

pirate (n) Johnny Depp is in the '*Pirates* of the Caribbean' films.

rope (n) My car is in the river. Have you got a strong *rope*?

storm (n) The small boats are staying at home today. The men can't work in a *storm*.

treasure (n) People sometimes find *treasure* in old boats under the sea.

website (n) The *website* address for Pearson English Readers is www.pearsonenglishreaders.com.

Answers for the Activities in this book are available from the Pearson English Readers website. A free Activity Worksheet is also available from the website. Activity worksheets are part of the Pearson English Readers Teacher Support Programme, which also includes Progress tests and Graded Reader Guidelines. For more information, please visit: www.pearsonenglishreaders.com

Pearson Education Limited
Edinburgh Gate, Harlow,
Essex CM20 2JE, England
and Associated Companies throughout the world.

ISBN: 978-1-4082-2116-7

This edition first published by Pearson Education Ltd 2010

8

Illustrations by Scott Altmann

Printed in Brazil by Docuprint DCPT 220206

Published by Pearson Education Ltd

For a complete list of the titles available in the Pearson English Readers series, please visit www.pearsonenglishreaders.com. Alternatively, write to your local Pearson Education office or to Pearson English Readers Marketing Department, Pearson Education, Edinburgh Gate, Harlow, Essex CM20 2JE, England.